Peter's Railway
Now and Then

by
Christopher Vine

The watercolour illustrations are by John Wardle

Published by
Christopher Vine 2012

Printed by The Amadeus Press
Copyright © 2012 Christopher Vine

ISBN 978-1-9088970-08

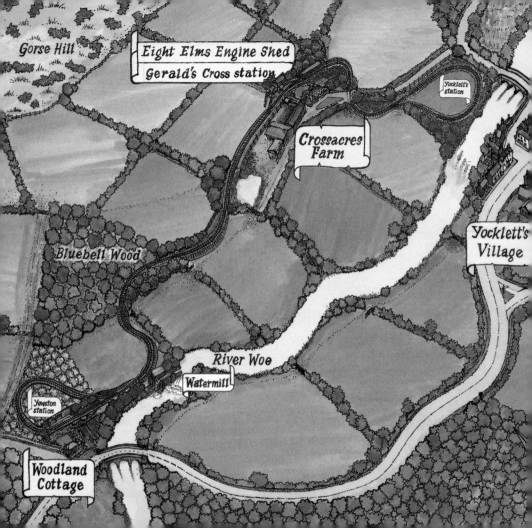

The Peter's Railway Series

The little steam railway runs across fields and links Peter and Grandpa's houses.

The locomotive, Fiery Fox, is a wonderful machine. Bright green and very powerful, it can pull heavy trains along the line at high speed. Many visitors to the railway have admired her and enjoyed their day out, but one visitor has a particularly good way to say 'Thank you.'

Recently Chris read a true story about a hair-raising night goods train, nearly a hundred years ago. Soon after, he was offered a cab ride in a modern freight locomotive. The differences inspired this book.

Now and Then

A letter dropped on the doormat. It was from Mr Otto, thanking Peter and Grandpa for a wonderful day out on their farm railway.

Mr Otto's day job, or more often night job, was driving a large and modern diesel locomotive, hauling freight trains all over the country.

"...In an attempt to repay your kindness," his letter finished, "please find enclosed two special tickets. They will allow you to accompany me in the cab of my locomotive, on a 300 mile round trip, next Tuesday night.

"We leave the depot at seven o'clock in the evening. I will come and collect you in my car at 5.30 pm..."

Grandpa was astounded and Peter was so excited he jumped up and down. But would Mum let him go? It would mean being out all night.

"Of course you can," she said. "You can't miss an adventure like this!"

Mr Otto, as good as his word, arrived in his car. Peter and Grandpa were ready and waiting.

The freight depot was lit up by floodlights on tall pylons. "You will have to wear these high visibility jackets," Mr Otto told them. "We've got to cross the yard to get to our engine."

Up close, the locomotive was enormous. Much bigger when you are on the ground and not standing high up on a station platform.

They climbed the steps to the dimly lit cab.

After tidying away their coats, there was still about 15 minutes before they were due to depart. "The first thing I have to do," explained Mr Otto, "is start the engine. It's good for it to warm up slowly."

He flicked some switches, then pushed a large button on the control console. Behind their backs, a soft whirring sound turned into a muted rumble as the huge diesel engine stirred into life.

As it warmed up, Mr Otto showed them all the different controls. The speed control lever, brakes, radio telephone, speedometer and more.

"The horn is your job Peter," he smiled, pointing to a little lever. "But only when I tell you! We've got 1500 tonnes behind us tonight, it's serious work."

While the engine was warming up, Mr Otto telephoned the controller to confirm that he was ready for duty, engine running. "You should be away on time," came the reply. "The line is clear."

While they were waiting for the signal in front of them to turn green, Mr Otto opened the driver's manual and showed them a diagram of the Class 66, diesel-electric locomotive.

"The main power unit is a 12 cylinder diesel engine," he explained. "It develops 3300 horsepower and drives an electric generator. The electricity is used to power the traction motors which turn the wheels."

Peter and Grandpa studied the book while the driver prepared for the night's work. The fuel tank contained over 1400 gallons of diesel!

Inside a Diesel-Electric Locomotive

A British Railways "Peak" Class 44 locomotive. 2300 Horsepower.

From an old BR training manual.

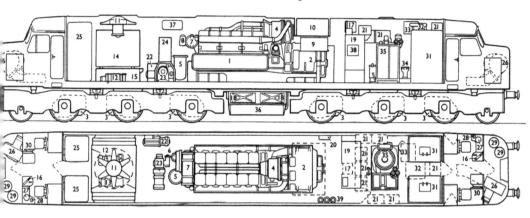

1	Diesel Engine	14	Radiator Panels
2	Main and Aux Generators	15	Radiator Drain Tank
3	Traction Motor	16	Master Controller
4	Turbo Charger	17	Voltage Regulator
5	Lubricating Oil Filter	18	Battery Boxes for starting
6	Lubricating Oil Strainer	19	Main Control Cubicle
7	Heat Exchanger	20	Instrument Cubicle
8	Engine Instrument Panel	21	Resistance Frames
9	Engine Air Filter	22	Air Compressor
10	Exhaust Silencer	23	Air Exhauster
11	Radiator Fan	24	Brake-Gear Cubicle
12	Combined Pump Set	25	Main Fuel Tank
13	Converter Set	26	Traction Motor Cooling Fan

27	Vacuum Brake Valve
28	Independent Air Brake Valve
29	Compressed Air Reservoirs
30	Handbrake Wheel
31	Boiler Water Feed Tank
32	Boiler Water Treatment Tank
33	Flush Tank for W.C.
34	W.C. (Lavatory)
35	Steam Generator for heating
36	Boiler Water Feed Tank
37	Fuel & Water Header Tank
38	Fuse Box
39	Fire Extinguisher Cylinders

At last the signal changed to green and a buzzer sounded in the cab. Mr Otto released the brakes and moved the power lever to 'slow'.

Behind them the engine note rose a little and the huge train crept forward, over the points and out onto the main line.

"Full power now," said Mr Otto, as he pushed the lever to its stop. The engine roared behind them and they surged forwards into the dusk. The engine note rising and falling as they worked up and down hills.

For an hour they powered along the track until a signal told them to stop. "We'll be stuck here for ages, I'm afraid," said Mr Otto, putting down the phone. "There's a blockage ahead."

It was cosy and warm in the cab so they settled down to pass the time, chatting.

"I've just finished reading an amazing book," said Grandpa. "It was the history of the old Glasgow & South Western Railway, in Scotland.

"There was one terrible story about a long and heavy goods train which split in two one dark night," he continued. "It was travelling on the line from Maybole down to Girvan, a hilly and undulating route.

"This was difficult for the driver," he explained, "because in those days the wagons didn't have proper brakes. The only working brakes were on the engine and the guard's van at the back. The driver and guard had to work together as a team to control the train."

"To make matters worse, the old fashioned wagons were only loosely coupled together with chains.

"With the engine pulling hard, all the chains would be stretched nice and tight. But if the driver braked or slowed down at the front, the wagons would catch up, one by one, the buffers banging and the chains between them going slack.

"That wasn't very good, but the trouble really started when the engine began pulling again and the chains pulled tight with a jolt.

"As the front part of the train got faster, the snatching got worse and worse at each wagon. If the driver wasn't careful it was easy to snatch a chain so badly that it would snap in two, leaving the rest of the train behind."

"Going south from Maybole," Grandpa continued with his story, "the line runs downhill for a couple of miles but then goes up for a short distance to Kilkerran, before going on down again.

"It was a difficult bit of driving because on the downhill parts, the train could catch up with the engine and the couplings go slack. Then, as the engine started pulling again up the next hill, the train would start to stretch out and snatch the chains tight. There was every risk of a disaster.

"The experienced drivers had worked out a system. They kept steam on for the downhill parts, to keep the coupling chains tight. The poor guard at the back would wind his hand brake on as hard as he could, to stop the train going too fast and getting out of control."

"Well, on the night in question," continued Grandpa, "there were two locomotives hauling the train. It was long and heavy with 54 wagons and the guard's van at the back.

"On the descent from Maybole for some reason, the driver of the leading engine didn't go fast enough. The train caught up with them and the couplings went slack. Then, when they hit the rise to Kilkerran, they felt a dreadful jolt.

"Surely the train had parted? But they couldn't be certain in the pitch black night. This was really dangerous now, as the rear part of the train could catch up again and smash into them.

"Was the train broken? They couldn't see the light on the guard's van, but with all the curves, trees and cuttings, it was hard to know."

"They went flat out up the hill and then flew down the other side, ever faster, trying to keep ahead of the back half of the train!

"At last there was a straight bit of track.

"Usually, coming down this hill you couldn't miss the guard's van. Flames and sparks would be flying from its burning brake blocks. Sometimes even its wooden floor caught alight!

"Tonight, nothing. The train must have split in two. If the back of the train had made it over the summit at Kilkerran, it couldn't be far behind them. They tore down the bank, whistles shrieking.

"They didn't dare stop until Girvan, some 10 miles further. Driver McGee ran back counting wagons. Only 28 wagons still attached, 26 more were somewhere out in the dark, running amok!"

"Where was the back half of the train?" Peter wanted to know. "And what did they do next?"

"Driver McGee rushed to the signal box at Girvan," replied Grandpa. "And after much frantic telephoning, they finally located the missing train at Kilkerran. The guard had walked back to the station and alerted the signalman there."

"Well," said Mr Otto, "I'm glad that driving trains isn't like that now. It must have been terrifying.

"Modern freight trains are completely different. Every single wagon behind us is tightly coupled together and fitted with brakes," he explained. "And, if the train should split in two for any reason, then all the brakes will go on automatically and bring everything to a safe stop."

Just then the buzzer sounded and the signal outside changed from red to green.

"Back to work now," said Mr Otto cheerfully, as he released the brakes and pushed the power lever forward. The engine roared as they accelerated along the track.

It was hard to believe there was 1500 tonnes behind them. It seemed effortless.

"What a brilliant adventure," said Peter, grinning.

"Let's hope it's not as exciting as your Grandpa's story!" laughed Mr Otto, as 3300 horsepower propelled them into the night.

The End.

Why Peter's Railway?

Since a very small boy, Chris has always loved everything mechanical, especially steam engines. The first workshop was in his bedroom where he made an electric go-kart aged 8, followed by a mini-bike powered by the engine from a petrol lawn mower.

He spent many holidays on a friend's farm where there was a miniature railway across a field and so started a love of making model steam locomotives. The latest is Bongo, 8 feet long and the inspiration for Fiery Fox in the books.

Chris wanted to share his love and knowledge of railways and engineering: Peter's Railway is the result.

Story   **Technical**   **Adventure**